# ✱✱INT

- This little book i
companion throug
bell-ringing.
- Learning to ring
brainiest of us – a lifetime long – and it does involve a bit of 'paper work' – but it should be fun!
- **SO** — if this is your book, keep it handy and work through it page by page (Three weeks to a page is reasonable progress).

  .......it cannot help you if you lose it
  or leave it in your pocket !!!!!

- **BUT REMEMBER** ~ This cannot be a substitute for a good teacher, ~ we cannot explain everything completely in such a small book, so ASK YOUR INSTRUCTOR to help with any bits you don't understand, ASK to be shown how things are done, ASK to be tested, ASK to be corrected!

- **DO NOT EXPECT** instant success or compliments ~you are more likely to be shouted at or criticised (with good reason) but please do not be put off....... your ringing will progress step by step. Tower captains and instructors often sound fierce or angry but be assured that There is no ill-feeling, it is simply That to correct faults requires fast and positive action ~ They care about your ringing, and your safety, and so....

- **GOOD LUCK** ~ turn The page and begin a life-time's fascinating hobby.....⟶

# INDEX + PROGRESS CHART

(tick each section here as you begin to work on it)

# Welcome, new bell-ringer!

You are beginning to learn an art which has been developed and passed from generation to generation in Britain for three hundred years. It is a wonderful blend of SPORT, MUSIC, EXERCISE, FRIENDSHIP, A CHALLENGE TO YOUR WITS AND SKILL, WONDERFUL SATISFACTION WHEN YOU GET IT RIGHT, AND A SERVICE TO THE CHURCH.

| Date of your first lesson | |
|---|---|
| Name of your instructor | |
| His/her phone no. or address | |

- Fill in these details, and the ones on the front cover.
- If you cannot go ringing at any time, or will be late, please let your instructor know so that time will not be wasted waiting for you.
- Show this book to friends and relations. Perhaps they too would like to 'join the band'.

# ✻ LOOK AT THE BELLS

When you begin to learn, your instructor will take you up to see the bells in their frame. The bells will be "down" but it may be safe for one to be "rung up" to demonstrate how it works

NEVER GO UP TO THE BELLS ALONE
NEVER GO NEAR BELLS WHICH ARE "UP"

Ask your instructor these questions:—

- Which is the biggest (tenor) bell?
- Which are the others, in order?
- Ask him to point out on a bell which is "down" all the parts listed on the next page

- Can you read any inscriptions? Bells are often very old, but generally they have been re-hung on ball-bearings in a modern frame. Have yours? (See page 10 for details to complete)

- Try to swing the clapper in a bell which is "down" (NEVER TOUCH AN 'UP' BELL ~ VERY DANGEROUS). Feel how heavy even the clapper is.

- Try to swing a bell which is 'down', a little bit, then stop it swinging ....... very heavy – much heavier than you are, therefore ringing must be by SKILL not BRUTE FORCE!

- When you learn to ring, at first a clapper tie will be put on to silence the bell (otherwise the neighbours begin to complain about the noise!). Ask to see how this is done and, if possible, learn to put it on and take it off, thus saving your instructor some work!

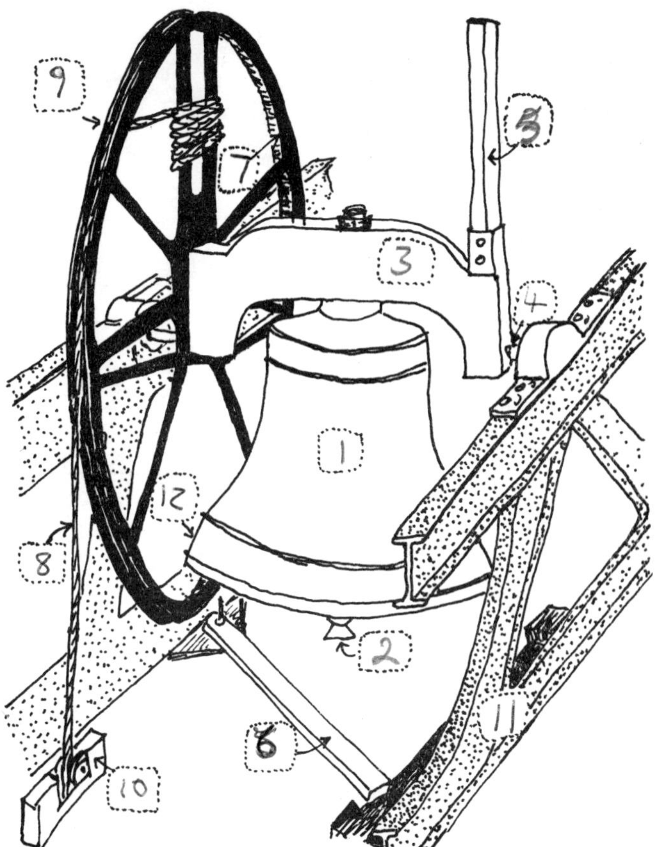


MARK THE NUMBERS OF THESE PARTS INTO THE DOTTED BOXES

| | | | |
|---|---|---|---|
| 1. Bell | 2. Clapper | 3. Headstock | 4. Gudgeon |
| 5 Stay | 6. Slider | 7. Wheel | 8 Rope |
| 9. Garter hole | 10. Pulley box | 11. Frame | 12. Sound bow |

Which bits are made of wood? Why? What kind of wood?

# Back-stroke
(=tail stroke)

WHAT THINGS ARE DIFFERENT? □□□□

1. ....................................................

2. ....................................................

3. ....................................................

4. ....................................................

Here is 'you' holding the bell on the balance at backstroke

## RULES TO REMEMBER AT BACKSTROKE

1. Keep hands together
2. Arms straight
3. Look ahead
4. Feet slightly apart
5. Pull should be:-
   - straight, vertical, close to body
   - gentle and even: just keep the rope tight & "feel your horses mouth"
   - all the way down, until your thumbs point downwards ~ try to throw the rope thro' a hole in floor at "X"
6. Catch the sally at about waist height and allow it to rise to the balance.

**First rang backstroke alone** [ date ]

# Hand-stroke
(=sally stroke)

On both strokes the 'DONG' sounds just as your hands pass your nose on the way up.

Here is 'you', holding the bell on the balance at hand-stroke

## RULES TO REMEMBER FOR THE HANDSTROKE

1,2,3 + 4 as for backstroke
5. Hold tail end in your left hand so that it lies in front of the sally (see sketch): put ALL your fingers round the sally.
6. Pull down straight, harder.
7. As soon as you let go the sally, transfer your right hand onto the tail, before your arms are taken up. Follow the tail up, keeping the rope taut and allow it to rise to the balance.

**First rang handstroke alone** ______ date

**✱ BOTH STROKES TOGETHER** will need a lot of help and practice. DON'T FORGET all the rules for each stroke

First rang both strokes, alone [ date ]

## ✱ SETTING THE BELL

You must learn to set the bell gently, without bashing the stay (which is only a 'safety valve')

1. Try out of 10 at handstroke [ /10 ]

2. Then 10 times backstroke [ /10 ]

3. Then 20 times hand & back [ /20 ]

(write in pencil so you can rub it out & put in a new number when you get better!)

(A chocolate bar rewards my learners if they ever honestly achieve this perfectly! - with witnesses!)

## ✱ FASTER AND SLOWER

You must learn to ring:—

faster — { take up a little tail end rope / catch the sally a bit higher

and

slower — { let out tail rope & catch the sally lower / but not so much that you touch the stay

PRACTICE 6 slow pulls then six faster strokes (look on page 20 to see why)

Rang 6 slow and six fast alternately 5 times .......... [ date ]

If you have the chance on tied bells also try this for other numbers eg. 8, counting "Slow 1-2-3-4-5-6-7-8 quicker 8-7-6-5-4-3-2-1"

## ✱ FOLLOWING........

You must learn to 'follow' another bell, leaving the right space. Really your **EARS** will tell you what is correct, but as a guide on tied bells the person you are following after must have pulled about half the length of his sally when you begin your pull.

- Allow the same gap at backstroke.
- It is important to develop a smooth, regular pull so that you can feel the rhythm.

## ✱ NOW SOME SERIOUS STUFF!

Ringing is fun, but it can be very dangerous ~ people have been severely injured or even killed ~ so LEARN these **SAFETY RULES** and be tested

1. Do as you are told – fast!
2. Keep your mind on the job -100%.
3. Never play around with the ropes.
4. Keep feet away from box edge.
5. Never walk near anyone ringing.
6. When sitting near someone who is ringing, keep both feet on floor.
7. Never ring a bell unless told you may.
8. Do not make a noise or lark about in the ringing chamber.
9. Never go up among the bells alone
10. and never go near a bell which is 'up'.

**✱ DON'T** always get stuck on the same bell. Practise on as many different bells as your teacher will allow. Keep a record here:-

| Bell | | Notes on history of bell. Who cast it? When? How does it feel to ring? |
|---|---|---|
| 1 "Treble" | date rung first | |
| | weight | How old is this bell? |
| 2 | date rung | |
| | weight | |
| 3 | date rung | |
| | weight | |
| 4 | date rung | |
| | weight | |
| 5 | date rung | |
| | weight | |
| 6 "Tenor" if you only have 6 bells | date rung | |
| | weight | |

Bell weights are given in Hundredweights (cwts.) Quarters (of a hundredweight) and Pounds (lbs.) 1 cwt. = 4 qu. = 112 lb. = 50·802 kg.

## ✱ PROGRESS REPORT

By the time you can control a tied bell well enough to join in the normal practices, your instructor will have spent many hours helping and teaching you. •The following space is for a serious (well quite serious!) report. It may save nagging later!....and it really is important to develop good habits and stamp out any bad ones quickly. (You may have to ask for this)

RINGING STYLE (mention bad habits to be cured).............

...............................................................

...............................................................

...............................................................

BELL CONTROL...............................................

...............................................................

...............................................................

...............................................................

BEHAVIOUR & SAFETY.....................................

...............................................................

...............................................................

ATTENDANCE..................................................

...............................................................

PUNCTUALITY.................................................

...............................................................

OTHER COMMENTS..........................................

...............................................................

signed (instructor)________________ (date)__________

## ✻ MAKING A NOISE

At last you will be ready for 'open' bells! When you join in the normal practice session all the other ringers will try to help you make quick progress. (Remember they were all once learners like you!) Listen to all their advice as sometimes a different person can identify your problem and help you cure it.

## ✻ RINGING ROUNDS......

'Rounds' is 123456 etc, down the scale.

~~~ OPEN YOUR EARS AND LISTEN! ~~~

Too many ringers never bother to listen – they go on ringing for ever with imaginary clapper-ties on their ears ~ and they never make good ringers!

• You must LISTEN and COUNT the bells. If you are on no. 3 bell then hear:-

| 1 | 2 | 3 | 4 | 5 | 6 | 1 | 2 | 3 | 4 | 5 | 6 | ■ | 1 | 2 | etc |
|---|---|---|---|---|---|---|---|---|---|---|---|---|---|---|---|

• Listen to the 'ding' in third place, which should be your bell. Accuracy to 1/16th of a second is necessary! If it all seems too quick, try fitting in "dee-da-dee-dadee-dum" and remember yours is the third one.

NOT | 1 | 23 | ■ | 4 | 5 | 6 | (You are too quick, too close to no 2)

NOR | 1 | 2 | ■ | 3 | 4 | 5 | 6 | (Too wide, too late)

LISTEN AND COUNT all the time!

• Adjust your speed until your bell sounds regularly in the right place. If you get badly out of place, hold your bell on the balance and wait. Ring EVENLY!

First rang rounds correctly... date
~~~

## ✱ THINGS TO DO while sitting out:-

• Silently watch other people ringing. Decide who has bad habits and who has the best style.

• All ringing starts and ends with rounds. Shut your eyes and LISTEN and COUNT. Can you hear the six (if there are six bells) beats ~ 1, 2, 3, 4, 5, 6? Which bells are striking badly? (or are they all correct). Are they early or late? Handstroke or backstroke? This is VERY DIFFICULT but well worth the effort: it will help develop your sense of rhythm so you will be able to strike your own bell correctly. You may find that some apparently very clever ringers are not actually striking their bells accurately.

• Now watch the ringers. Can you see who is leading? Can you see who is last? Watch one ringer and notice the point at which his bell sounds.

## ✱ NAMES OF METHODS

• Listen to the names ~ "Grandsire Doubles", "Cambridge Surprise Minor," "Oxford Bob Triples", "Kent Treble Bob Major." Always the 'surname' tells you how many bells are changing places. Odd bell methods (on 3, 5, 7 etc) usually have the tenor last (covering) in each change if there are an even number of bells. Tick the ones below which could be rung in your home tower. (Learn the names by heart ♥♥♥♥♥♥ Tick tested O.K!)

| | | | |
|---|---|---|---|
| ☐ | 3 bells ring SINGLES | ☐ | 4 bells ring MINIMUS |
| ☐ | 5 bells ring DOUBLES | ☐ | 6 bells ring MINOR |
| ☐ | 7 bells ring TRIPLES | ☐ | 8 bells ring MAJOR |
| ☐ | 9 bells ring CATERS | ☐ | 10 bells ring ROYAL |
| ☐ | 11 bells ring CINQUES ("sinks"!) | ☐ | 12 bells ring MAXIMUS |

# ✱ CALLED CHANGES

will be your next lesson. To change the tune from rounds the conductor will 'call changes'. Each call swaps over an adjacent pair of bells.

Thus from rounds the call "2 and 3 change" gives

132456

The call is made on one handstroke and the bells should change over cleanly at the next handstroke.

- Different conductors and different towers call in a number of different ways, but the result is always the same. Be warned and keep concentrating!
- Here are four other ways of calling the above change

| | | |
|---|---|---|
| from 123456 | "2 to 3"<br>"3 to 1"<br>"2,3"<br>132456 | all result in 132456 |

- Always three bells have to think what to do. In the above example
  - "2" has to hold up slower and follow bell "3"
  - "3" has to ring quicker, after "1" (ie. the bell 2 had been following)
  - "4" stays at same speed but after 2 not 3
- Try to HEAR the different tune after every change is called. Work out which bell is yours by its place.

- Continuing the changes from 132456

| | |
|---|---|
| call "4 and 5 change" gives | 132546 |
| "2 and 5 change" → | 135246 "queens" |
| 5 and 2 change | 132546 |
| 3 and 2 change | 123546 |
| 4 and 5 change | 123456 "rounds" |

See which three bells have to follow a new bell each time a change is called. We called the bells into 'Queens'.

• Now we will call the bells into another order: 142536, called "TITTUMS" (because its tune sounds 'ti-tum-ti-tum-ti-tum). You write the changes into the boxes:–

| | | | | | | |
|---|---|---|---|---|---|---|
| Start from rounds | | | | | | |
| call "3 to 4" | | | | | | |
| "3 to 5" | | | | | | |
| This is "tittums" → "2 to 4" | | | | | | |
| ............ | | | | | | |
| ............ | | | | | | |
| ............ | | | | | | |
| ............ | | | | | | |
| ............ | | | | | | |
| | | | | | | |

Now you make up some different changes to get the bells back to rounds. Remember only next-door pairs can change places

• When you have understood this show it to the Tower Captain and ask if you may try calling it.

## ✱ LEADING

- Sooner or later you will find you are called to lead (ie. ring first). To do this, you must follow the last bell (usually 6), on the OPPOSITE STROKE (your sally follows his tail & v.v.) LISTEN until you can hear your bell clearly first. One tip which may help is that the sound of the tenor (6) should coincide with the lowest point of your pull (when your thumbs point to the floor) DONG!

• There must be a one beat pause before your hand-stroke lead giving an over-all beat (on 6 bells) of 13.

→hand →back →hand →back →ha

▨ 1 2 3 4 5 6 1 2 3 4 5 6 ▨ 1 2 3 4 5 6 1 2 3 4 5 6 ▨ 1

# *VISITING

When you can ring rounds and called changes safely with reasonably good striking, try to visit some other towers on their practice nights or for meetings of your local Bellringers Guild. Your instructor will suggest where you could go and will probably go with you at first.

• Always make sure that the Tower Captain of any tower you visit knows your capabilities (or lack of them!) and always wait to be asked before catching hold of a rope to ring.

• There is a wonderful book by a man called DOVE which lists every tower in the world with bells hung for full circle ringing (over 5000 of them!) Ask your instructor to show you a copy. Ringers are great visitors and every tower, indeed every bell, is different. Your style and confidence will improve with every one you visit, and you will always be welcome.

• Keep a record of towers you ring at:-

| NO | DATE | CHURCH | NO. OF BELLS | WEIGHT |
|---|---|---|---|---|
| 1 | | | | |
| 2 | | | | |
| 3 | | | | |
| 4 | | | | |
| 5 | | | | |
| 6 | | | | |
| 7 | | | | |
| etc. | | | | |

# ✱METHOD RINGING 'scientific-ringing' 'change-ringing'

Some bands only ever ring 'called changes', generally very well struck indeed. In Cornwall and Devon most of the towers only ring called changes.

•However in most places you will find 'method ringing' where the bells change every pull according to a known pattern, or method. There are hundreds of different methods but PLAIN BOB and GRANDSIRE are the most frequently rung. Method ringing began to evolve from called changes in about 1650.

•Here are two exercises to help you to get used to moving your bell about quickly. Good bell control is essential!

FIRST EXERCISE ~ PLACE-MAKING

B 1 2 3 4 5 6
H 2 1 3 4 5 6
B 2 1 3 4 5 6
H 1 2 3 4 5 6
B 1 2 3 4 5 6
H 2 1 3 4 5 6
B 2 1 3 4 5 6 etc

- a) Draw different coloured lines through bells 1, 2 & 3 (follow dots)
- b) Ring no 3 bell, keeping it in a steady speed over 1 and 2.
- c) Ring 1 or 2 who are "making places" (which means a whole pull in lead & a whole pull in 2nd place over the other bell, repeatedly)

SECOND EXERCISE ~ DODGING

B 1 2 3 4 5 6
H 2 1 3 4 5 6
B 1 2 3 4 5 6
H 2 1 3 4 5 6
B 1 2 3 4 5 6
H 2 1 3 4 5 6

- a) Draw coloured lines again
- b) Ring no. 3 bell as before
- c) Ring 1 or 2 who are 'dodging' with each other (crossing over at handstroke and returning to rounds at backstroke.

LISTEN and COUNT all the time. The rhythm should be perfect even when the bells are changing, 1 2 3 4 5 6 etc.

# ✱ PLAIN HUNTING

Plain hunting is the basis of all method ringing. This you must master first. It is like weaving or plaiting!

| | | | | |
|---|---|---|---|---|
| "Go Plain Hunting" | | 1 | 2 | 3 |
| | H | 2 | 1 | 3 |
| | B | 2 | 3 | 1 |
| | H | 3 | 2 | 1 |
| | B | 3 | 1 | 2 |
| | H | 1 | 3 | 2 |
| "That's all" | B | 1 | 2 | 3 |

On 3 bells it is called "PLAIN HUNT SINGLES" (see page 13)

Every bell changes by one place every stroke until it reaches last or first place, where it must stay for two strokes.

| | | | |
|---|---|---|---|
| 1 | 2 | 3 | 4 |
| 2 | 1 | | 3 |
| 2 | | 1 | 3 |
| | 2 | 3 | 1 |
| | 3 | 2 | 1 |
| 3 | | 1 | 2 |
| 3 | 1 | | 2 |
| 1 | 3 | 2 | |
| 1 | 2 | 3 | 4 |

On 4 bells it is Plain Hunt Minimus

- In all these examples draw different colour lines through the path of each bell to make the pattern show up.
- In The Minimus, write in The number 4 bell

| | | | | |
|---|---|---|---|---|
| 1 | 2 | 3 | 4 | 5 |
| 2 | | 4 | | |
| 2 | 4 | | | |
| 4 | 2 | | | |
| 4 | | 2 | | |
| | 4 | | 2 | |
| | | 4 | | 2 |
| | | | 4 | 2 |
| | | | 2 | 4 |
| | | 2 | | 4 |
| 1 | 2 | 3 | 4 | 5 |

On 5 bells it is PLAIN HUNT DOUBLES

- In The Doubles you have to complete The paths of 1, 3 and 5
- Draw coloured lines again. Try to keep The same colour for The same bell each time.
- Finish all this quickly Then go on.

THIS PAGE CORRECTLY FILLED IN [ date ]

| 1 | 2 | 3 | 4 | 5 | 6 |
|---|---|---|---|---|---|
| | | | | | |
| | | | | | |
| | | | | | |
| | | | | | |
| | | | | | |
| | | | | | |
| | | | | | |
| | | | | | |
| | | | | | |
| | | | | | |
| | | | | | |
| 1 | 2 | 3 | 4 | 5 | 6 |

On 6 bells, PLAIN HUNT MINOR

- Complete this block and join up all the bells' paths in different colours.

- Before you can begin to actually ring this there are several things you should understand about it so carry on now through this page & the first part of page 20.

- Look first at the path which the no 1 bell (treble) has followed.

GOING UP

} LYING (AT THE BACK)

GOING DOWN

} LEADING (AT THE FRONT)

- Words we use

In Plain Hunting, a bell hunts UP to the BACK, LIES there for two blows, then hunts DOWN to the FRONT, where it LEADS for two blows.

- Study the PLAIN HUNT MINOR above and answer the following questions :— ***How many bells sound between your bell ringing and your bell ringing again*** .........

........a) In rounds ___ ☐
b) Going up ___ ☐
c) Lying behind__ ☐
d) Coming down__ ☐
e) Leading____ ☐

} does this suggest that your speed of ringing must vary?

answers p.20

• It is quite helpful to think of this as a flight of steps, or a mountain. You go up it slowly and down fast! In fact just what you were practicing on page eight.

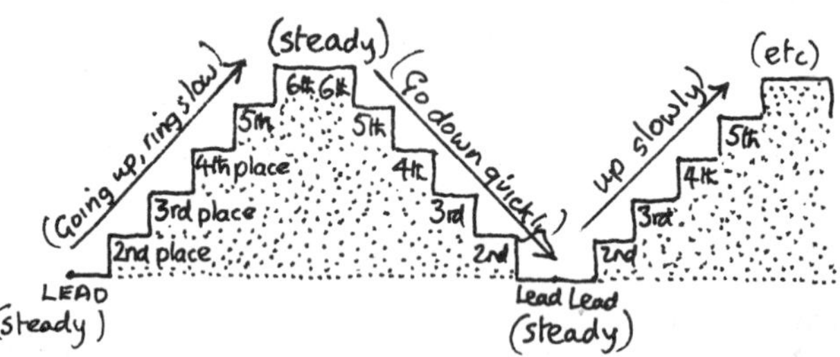


• As soon as you reach this point, go and stand behind someone who is plain hunting the treble (many methods, like Grandsire & Plain Bob have the treble plain hunting & it does not matter very much to you what the other bells are doing.) Ask the treble ringer to count his places out loud and you count too, till eventually you can keep counting correctly up and down on your own. Assuming it is on 6 bells (minor) ~ but you could similarly do doubles or any other number of working places :-

"2nd place" (watch them hold up the sally stroke to wait for another bell to ring before them)
"3rd place" (hold up slow again, at tail-stroke)
"4th place" (slow at sally stroke)
"5th place" (and slow at tail)
"6th place" (slow again at sally stroke - now last, lying)
"6th place" (steady at backstroke)
"5th place" (cut in quickly at sally, coming down)
"4th place" (quickly at tail-stroke)
"3rd place" (quickly at sally-stroke)
"2nd place" (and quickly again at tail)
"Lead" (quickly at sally stroke but pulling harder
"Lead" to hold up steady for second blow in lead
"2nd place" and then begin the slow going up again.)

---

Answers to p.19 questions a) 5, b) 6, c) 5, d) 4, e) 5. Yes (see p. 8 too)

• When you have counted this out loud on your own for several times correctly, ask the ringer you were standing behind to sign here :–

| sign | date |
|---|---|
| | |

COUNTED PLAIN HUNTING CORRECTLY

• You should by now realise that ringing is a matter of RHYTHM. A blind person can ring well (several do, their guide dogs tied up safely nearby), but a deaf person would not manage at all well. And considering what a loud noise church bells make, it is surprising but true that some people with otherwise perfect hearing "switch off their ears" when ringing. You will hear people say, "I cannot hear my bell" ~ and the reason is that they forgot to listen in the early stages. They are never the best ringers as they cannot compensate for odd-struck bells. The secret is to listen for the POSITION which you bell is in, you do not have to recognise its <u>note</u> amongst the others. If you are in 3rd place you must hear

✱ ✱ <u>YOU</u> ✱ ✱ ✱

• So, when sitting out, SHUT YOUR EYES and listen to the bells. Assuming that there are six,

1. Can you hear the six bell beat and count
   123456123456 ▨ 123456123456 ▨ 12 etc
   ↑ pause before handstroke lead.
2. Now count the places of the treble while it is plain hunting, just like you did at the top of this page, but with your EYES SHUT. It is <u>not easy</u> but you must persist until you can hear it quite clearly. Sign the box for yourself when you can!

| |
|---|
| |

COUNTED, EYES CLOSED!

• Thats all very well in theory but now you must actually ring it. Its normally best to begin on the Treble but if your instructor asks you to go on another bell don't be dismayed. Just remember the idea of steps, find out which step you are starting on and whether you begin by going up or down. <u>Even</u> number bells go <u>down</u> first and odd numbers go <u>up</u>. Every bell begins on its own step (or place).

THUS 3 begins in <u>3rd</u> place, & being <u>odd</u> goes <u>UP</u>.

2 begins in ........place and goes ...........

4 begins in .......place and goes ..........

(Fill these in and ask someone to check if right.)

• Each step is over a number of bells, (just like if you were 3rd in a queue at a shop there would be 2 people in front of you, if you are ringing in 3rd place then two other ropes must pull before yours. When you move into 4th place those two <u>and</u> <u>one</u> <u>other</u> go in front of you and so on.

GO UP SLOW
GO DOWN FAST
GO UP SLOW

| LEAD | 2nd | 3rd | 4th | 5th | 6th | 6th | 5th | 4th | 3rd | 2nd | Lead | Lead | 2nd | 3rd | 4th | etc |
|---|---|---|---|---|---|---|---|---|---|---|---|---|---|---|---|---|
| | H | B | H | B | H | B | H | B | H | B | H | B | H | B | H | |

Yes, you do have to think fast! but gradually it will become easy, like learning to swim or ride a bike!

• We have illustrated PLAIN HUNT MINOR, (on 6 bells) but you may be asked to ring it on any other number of bells, on 5 it is called PLAIN HUNTING ———————, on 4 ————————, on 7 bells ———————— (here the tenor usually 'covers' & rings at the end of every change), or 8 bells —————— . Check your answers on page 13.

# ✱ GOOD STRIKING

• On the following two pages we have explained the idea of ROPE-SIGHT. Ropesight means looking at the other ropes and deciding which person to follow at every pull. It is useful and important BUT your ringing must primarily be smooth and steady, with rhythm. After all it is disaster to follow another person accurately if that person is in fact lost or out of place! AND to make matters more difficult, bells are often a bit peculiar in <u>when</u> they sound. We call this ODD-STRUCK. A bell may sound early at sally stroke and late at tail, or vice versa, just by how the clapper is fixed in the bell. If therefore you follow the oddstruck bell by rop<u>esi</u>ght the two ropes might <u>look</u> the right distance apart but they will <u>sound</u> too close or too wide.

• When you begin to ring anything the conductor will leave the bells in rounds for a minute or two before starting the changes. This is TO ALLOW THE RHYTHM TO SETTLE DOWN. **YOU** must work out which sound is **your** bell and adjust your pull at sally and tail until it is correct. If your bell is oddstruck in rounds it will continue to be odd struck in changes and you must continue to apply the same correction at sally and tail all through the ringing.

# ✱ ROPESIGHT

Imagine you are ringing the treble, plain hunting it to a DOUBLES method. This means that 2,3,4&5 will be doing rather more complicated things and the tenor, 6 (if there is one) will be covering (BONG! at the end of every change). The other ropes in the initial rounds will look like this:–

You are leading

2 3 4 5 6

Then the conductor says "Go, Plain Bob Doubles". LOOK ROUND, FIND THE BELL WHICH IS FOLLOWING YOU (OBVIOUSLY NO 2 BELL IN ROUNDS!) HOLD YOUR BELL UP AT SALLY STROKE AND FOLLOW THAT BELL. AT THE SAME TIME LOOK AT ALL THE OTHERS

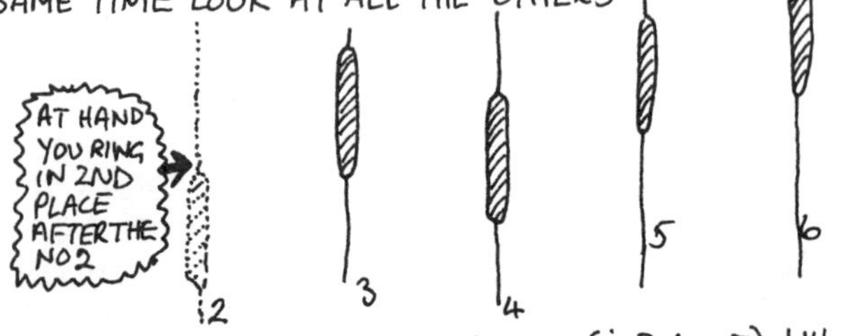


LOOKING AT THE REMAINING BELLS (ie 3,4+5), WHO IS NOW FOLLOWING YOU? NOT THE NO. 3 (who is going out to the back) BUT THE 4 (who comes down to lead). HOLD UP AT TAILSTROKE TO FOLLOW AFTER THE 4. AT THE SAME TIME LOOK AT THE REMAINING BELLS (3+5)

You don't have to worry about no 6 bell as it is only a doubles method so the tenor stays last all the time.

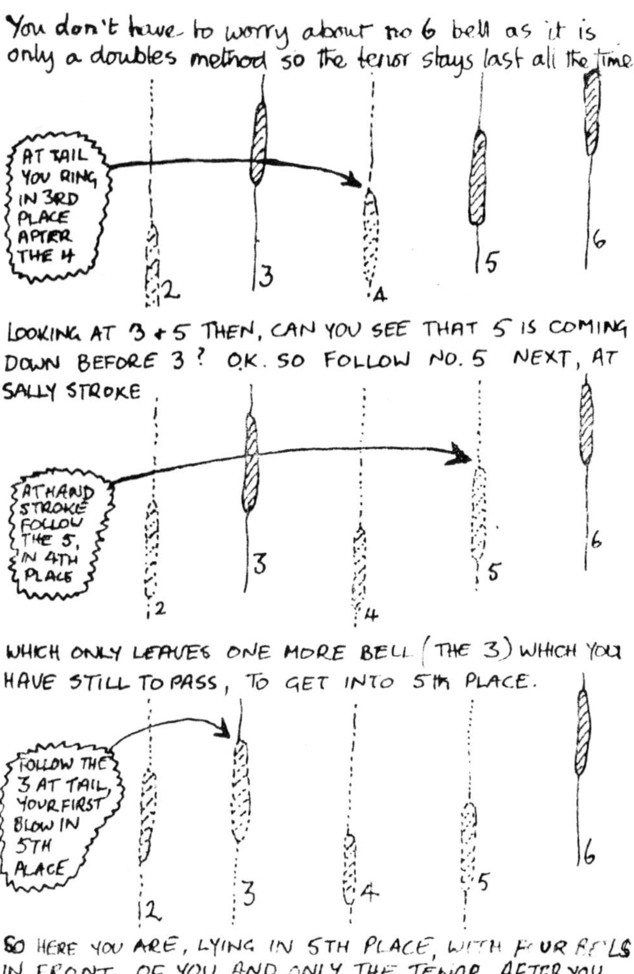


LOOKING AT 3 + 5 THEN, CAN YOU SEE THAT 5 IS COMING DOWN BEFORE 3? O.K. SO FOLLOW NO. 5 NEXT, AT SALLY STROKE



WHICH ONLY LEAVES ONE MORE BELL (THE 3) WHICH YOU HAVE STILL TO PASS, TO GET INTO 5TH PLACE.



SO HERE YOU ARE, LYING IN 5TH PLACE, WITH FOUR BELLS IN FRONT OF YOU AND ONLY THE TENOR AFTER YOU

| 2 | 4 | 5 | 3 |
|---|---|---|---|
| 2nd place | 3rd place | 4th place | 5th place |

ringing slowly

NOW RETURN TO LEAD FOLLOWING THEM IN THE *SAME ORDER

| 2 | 4 | 5 | 3 |
|---|---|---|---|
| 5th place | 4th place | 3rd place | 2nd Place |

ringing quickly!

THEN **LEAD** STEADILY, watching the tenor & following him at opposite stroke. Hand and back, THEN start all over again, holding up for the first bell, which may be a different one unless you are all plain hunting.

---

**✱ COURSING ORDER** This is the name given to the way the bells follow each other down to lead. It is a useful idea to grasp because in most methods it is also the order in which you pass the bells as you hunt through them, up & down. It stays the same except at a BOB or SINGLE. The bell who leads just before you is your COURSE BELL & the one who takes you off lead is your AFTER BELL.

- In Plain hunt minor the coursing order is 24653
- When you lead on the Treble in Plain Bob MINOR your course bell cuts round and becomes your after bell as it makes 2nds (see p 28). So the coursing order stays the same but you have to keep putting the back bell to the front until the whole cycle comes back to the beginning. 24653 then 32465 then 53246 then 65324, 46532 and back to 24653, at the end of a plain course.

---

*except in some more complicated methods.

## ✳ Now a **QUIZ** to test your understanding!

(underline the correct answer)

1. What is the name of all methods rung on 6 working bells?
   a) DOUBLES  b) MAJOR  c) MINOR  d) TRIPLES

2. Where do some ringers always seem to wear imaginary 'clapper ties'? (You don't, of course!)
   a) ON THEIR EYES  b) EARS  c) NECK  d) TONGUE

3. On both sally and tail stroke how far apart should your hands be?  a) 15cm APART  b) ABOUT 8cm  c) TOUCHING

4. In rounds, all bells should sound evenly spaced except for a 'one-bell-gap' before the Treble leads. When?
   a) AT HANDSTROKE  b) AT BACKSTROKE  c) BOTH STROKES

5. To ring faster you must
   a) PULL HARDER  b) TAKE UP TAIL  c) LET OUT TAIL

6. The purpose of the stay is (2 answers)
   a) TO BUMP THE BELL BACK IF YOU PULL TOO HARD
   b) TO HOLD THE BELL IN POSITION WHEN IT IS SET
   c) TO BREAK (AS A 'SAFETY VALVE') IF BELL IS OVER-PULLED

7. In called changes the instruction is given at a handstroke and you do it:  a) IMMEDIATELY  b) GRADUALLY  c) NEXT HANDSTROKE  d) NEXT BACKSTROKE

8. In rounds, if you hear ① ② ③  ④⑤ ⑥
   a) 5 IS RINGING TOO QUICKLY  b) 4 IS TOO SLOW  c) 3 IS TOO QUICK

9. In plain hunting, coming down from the back to lead you must
   a) RING FASTER  b) RING SLOWER  c) KEEP THE SAME SPEED

10. At the end of a piece of ringing the conductor calls 'stand'
    a) BECAUSE IF ANY RINGER WAS LEANING AGAINST THE WALL HE MIGHT FALL OVER WHEN THE ROPE STOPS GOING UP AND DOWN
    b) TO TELL THE RINGERS TO SET THEIR BELLS
    c) SO THAT THOSE RINGERS SITTING OUT CAN GET READY

11. In plain hunt doubles, your two blows lying in 5th place are  a) HAND-BACK  b) BACK-HAND  c) BOTH HANDSTROKE

12. The coursing order in Plain Hunt Doubles is
    a) 2345  b) 2435  c) 2543  d) 2453

---

1-c, 2-b, 3-c, 4-a, 5-b, 6-b+c, 7-c, 8-b, 9-a, 10-b, 11-b, 12-d.

# ✱ PLAIN BOB

Well, Plain Hunting eventually becomes a bit boring, so ringers have invented a number of Methods to make it go on for longer before coming back into rounds. The easiest method is Plain Bob. It can be rung on any number of bells from 4 to 12. see p. 13.

On SIX bells it is PLAIN BOB ________.

On FIVE bells it is PLAIN BOB ________.

The basic rule is always the same:-

"PLAIN HUNT UNTIL THE TREBLE GETS BACK TO LEAD. THEN LET THE BELL WHICH IS IN SECOND PLACE STAY THERE FOR ANOTHER BLOW OVER THE LEADING TREBLE THEN RETURN TO LEAD. (called "make seconds".) THIS FORCES EVERYONE ELSE TO STEP ONE PLACE BACK (called a "dodge") THEN EVERYONE CARRIES ON PLAIN HUNTING UNTIL THE TREBLE GETS BACK TO LEAD AGAIN. etc"

Draw coloured lines thro' each bell

3 5 1 6 2 4
3 1 5 2 6 4
1 3 2 5 4 6

PLAIN HUNT UNTIL THE TREBLE IS IN LEAD

1 3 5 2 6 4

← THE BELL IN 2ND PLACE (ie 3) STAYS THERE AND ALL OTHER BELLS (ie. 2, 5, 6 & 4) DODGE BACK ONE PLACE

3 1 2 5 4 6
3 2 1 4 5 6
2 3 4 1 6

EVERYONE CARRIES ON PLAIN HUNTING

Learn the rule and be tested.... [ ] date

•Here is a complete PLAIN COURSE of PLAIN BOB DOUBLES

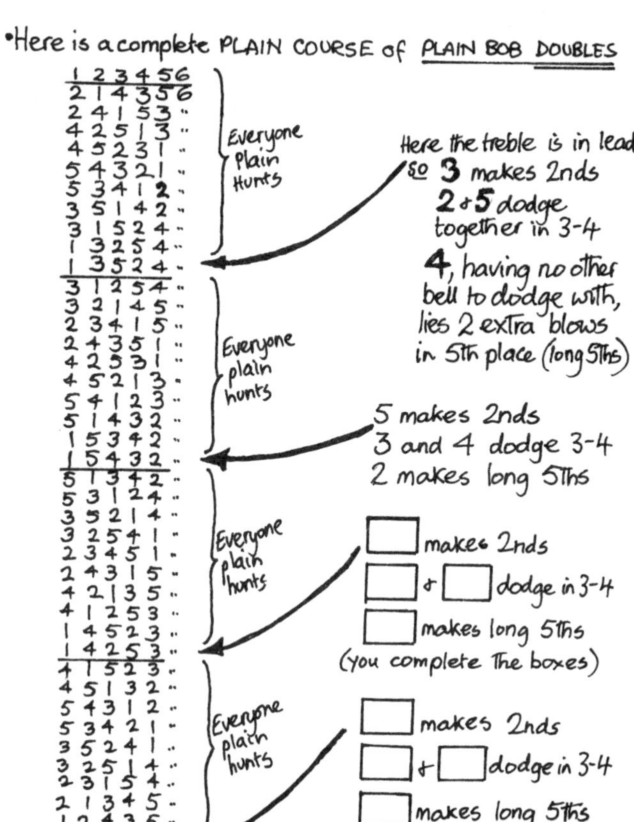


"Thats all", it has come back into rounds.

•Draw a red line through the treble's path, a blue line thro' no: 2 and all the others different colours. SEE ALSO P.T.O.

First rang Plain Bob on an inside bell [date]

• Here is the line you drew through bell no 2 on the previous page, but squashed up to take less space. Called "the blue line" it is a most useful ringers short-hand.

**PLAIN BOB DOUBLES**

1 2 3 4 5

(except Treble)

**explanation of work**

Plain hunt as far as 3rd place on the way down to lead

Dodge back up to 4th place (we call this dodge 3-4 down because you are on your way down)

Hunt up to 5th place and stay there for 4 blows (long fifths)

Hunt on as far as 4th place going up, then dodge back to 3rd place (i.e. dodge 3-4 up)

Hunt as far as 2nd place going up stay there for 2 blows (make 2nds)

• Every bell (except Treble) does the same work but all start at a different point along this line, thus we can draw a cycle of work.

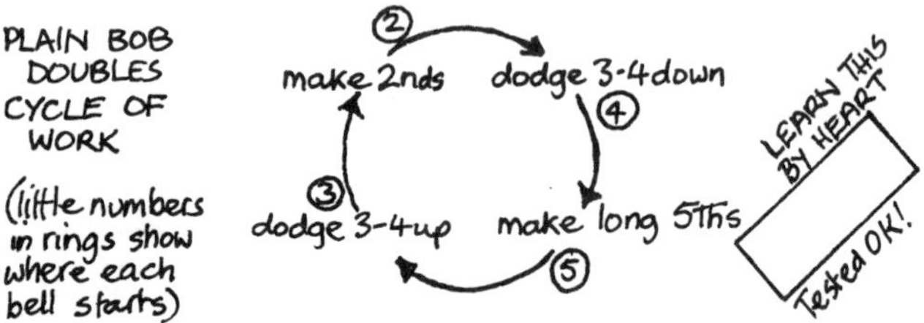


• So you must learn the order of work to be done, and listen for the Treble's lead. Another help is to notice each time you go up from lead WHERE YOU PASS THE TREBLE. This too gives you a useful set of rules to help you know which piece of work comes next. The more guides you have to help you the better ~ "belt and braces!"

• RULES FOR PASSING THE TREBLE IN P.B. DOUBLES

| YOU PASS THE TREBLE | ∴ NEXT WORK |
|---|---|
| in 5th place | dodge 3-4 down |
| in 4th place | make long 5ths |
| in 3rd place | dodge 3-4 up |
| in 2nd place | make 2nds |

← LEARN BY "♡" Tested OK!

rang P.B. doubles 'inside'.... without help!!! date

# ✱ BOBS

The plain course takes just over one minute to ring, and has only 40 different changes (lines). There are many other changes (different orders) and by calling BOBs the conductor can include more different changes before returning to rounds. (see next page to calculate how many changes are possible). BOB is called just before the treble leads and it causes the bells to do different work, as the following chart shows:-

| WORK YOU WERE GOING TO DO IF NO BOB CALLED (i.e. PLAIN LEAD) | PLACE YOU ARE IN AT BOB | NEW WORK YOU DO BECAUSE OF THE BOB | NEXT PIECE OF WORK (UNLESS ANOTHER BOB) |
|---|---|---|---|
| make 2nds | lead | hunt straight out to the back (run out) | make 2nds |
| dodge 3-4 down | 4th ↓ | hunt straight down to lead (run in) | dodge 3-4 down |
| long 5ths | 5th | long 5ths unaffected | dodge 3-4 up |
| dodge 3-4 up | 3rd ↑ | hunt up to 4th place then back to lead | long 5ths |

5 4 3 2 1
5 3 4 1 2
3 5 1 4 2
BOB CALL → 3 1 5 2 4
1 3 2 5 4
1 2 3 5 4
2 1 5 3 4
2 5 1 4 3
5 2 4 1 3
5 4 2 3 1

in this example

2 runs in instead of doing 3-4 down
3 runs out instead of making 2nds
5 makes 4ths instead of 3-4 up
4 makes long 5ths unaffected

(draw coloured lines to make this clear)

# A "TOUCH"

What a lot of odd words are used in campanology! This means using calls of BOB and/or SINGLE to change the order from the plain course and, without repeating any other changes, bring it back to rounds.

• On 5 working bells (ie. doubles) there are 120 possible different changes: if we ring them each once it is called the 'extent'. The extent on any number of bells can be calculated thus:-

On 5 = 5 x 4 x 3 x 2 x 1 ie 120 changes
On 6 = 6 x 5 x 4 x 3 x 2 x 1 ie. ☐ } What is the extent on 7? ☐

• So now to ring 120 changes of Plain Bob Doubles: one plain course is 40 changes long so we need three courses without repetition. A BOB affects three bells, changing each onto one of the others' path.

Thus A swaps onto B's path, B to C and C to A

It's a bit like imagining a triangle which is 'clicked round' one point at the first bob, another at the second and returns to its original position at the third.

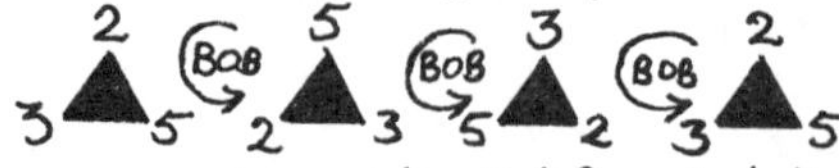


In the above example we have left out bell no 4 as this bell will be "unaffected", making long 5ths at each bob in your first touch. We call this the OBSERVATION BELL. Notice on the next page how the 4 is back in 4th place at the end of each of the three courses of your touch, but 3, 5 & 2 change.

The observation bell is the easiest one to ring as you will simply ring 3 plain courses, but after each bob you find you have a different bell to dodge with, until you come back to your original partner.

• Draw coloured lines thro' all the bells in the example opposite and study it very carefully. Then write out 120 making one of the other bells (eg. 2nd) observation. **Date box when done......** ☐ date

(i.e. a touch of 120 changes)
Here then are the Three courses of Plain Bob Doubles. each with a BOB called when 4 is making long 5ths (i.e. observation bell)

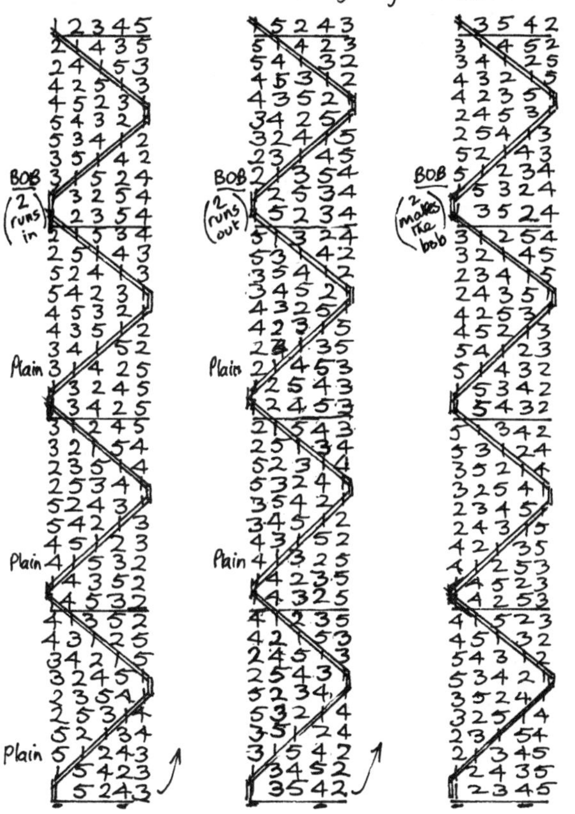

Rang 120 on observation bell; date →

Rang 120 on a bell which did the work →

# ✱ PLAIN BOB MINOR

Because there are now six bells changing, there is room for a pair of bells to dodge in 5-6 instead of just one bell lying in long 5ths at each lead end.

- As there is no covering tenor you must learn to LEAD OFF THE LAST BELL DOWN, WHICHEVER IT IS, AND LISTEN!!!
- Here is the line, with rules for passing the treble (each bell's start is shown in a circle)

1 2 3 4 5 6

Pass the Treble in 6th place going up
so dodge in 3-4 down

(4)

Pass treble in 5th place going up
so dodge in 5-6 down

(6)

Pass treble in 4th place going up
so dodge 5-6 up

(5)

Pass treble in 3rd place going up
so dodge 3-4 up

(3)

Treble turns you from lead
so make 2nds (and lead again)

- Learn this thoroughly before you try to ring it.
- Find a bigger piece of paper and write out the whole course.

Here is the CYCLE OF WORK for Plain Bob Minor (fill in the boxes like the one for Plain Bob Doubles on p.30)

- Ask someone to check that you've done it right
- Then LEARN IT!

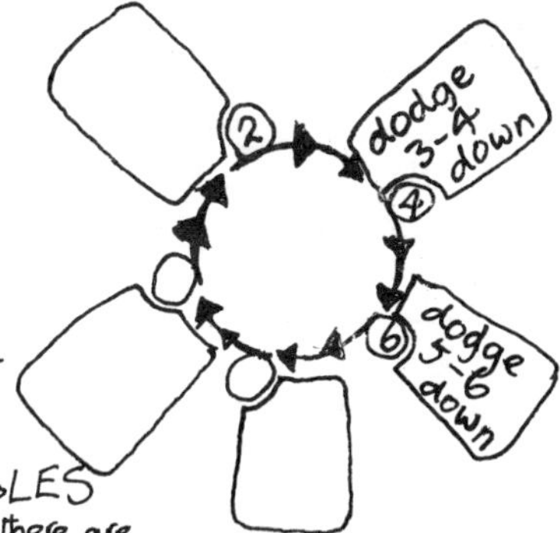


## BOBS & SINGLES

In Plain Bob Minor there are two kinds of call ~ BOBS (which change over 3 bells, and SINGLES (which only change over a single pair, i.e. 2 bells). Bobs are the same as in Bob Doubles; the two bells in 5-6 are unaffected. Singles are different for 2 bells, only.

WORK AT A BOB

| What you would do at Plain Lead | if a BOB is called | Then next work |
|---|---|---|
| 2nds | run out | 2nds |
| 3-4 down | run in | 3-4 down |
| 3-4 up | 4ths (make the Bob) | 5-6 down |
| 5-6 down | unaffected | |
| 5-6 up | " | |

WORK AT A SINGLE

| Work you would have done | single called | next work |
|---|---|---|
| 2nds | unaffected | |
| 3-4 down | 3rds from back | 2nds |
| 3-4 up | 4ths | 5-6 down |
| 5-6 down | unaffected | |
| 5-6 up | unaffected | |

✱ And now for a new method :–

GRANDSIRE DOUBLES is a great deal more complicated than Plain Bob, but it is often one of the first methods to be learnt. Now you understand ringers 'shorthand' all you have to do is learn the line and the rules.'

Basically Grandsire is like Plain Bob but with 2 bells plain hunting (the treble and one other bell, 2 in the plain course), so you must make 3rds when the treble turns you from lead, and the dodges are moved up to 4-5.

THE PLAIN COURSE

1 2 3 4 5

← Make 3rds

← Pass treble in 4th place

← so dodge 4-5 down

← Pass Treble in 3rd place

← So dodge 4-5 up

← Treble turns you from lead

← so make 3rds

CYCLE OF WORK

3rds → dodge 4-5 down → dodge 4-5 up → 3rds

Tip for Grandsire Doubles: Pass treble, pass one more & dodge with the next bell. Then treble again.

WORK AT BOB

WORK AT SINGLE

| PLAIN LEAD | WORK AT A BOB | NEXT WORK |
|---|---|---|
| In the hunt | Double dodge in 4-5 down | 4-5 up |
| 4-5 down | Double dodge 4-5 up | 3rds |
| 4-5 up | Make early thirds | In the hunt |
| 3rds | unaffected | |

| PLAIN LEAD | WORK AT A SINGLE | NEXT WORK |
|---|---|---|
| In the hunt | same as bob | |
| 4-5 down | " " " | |
| 4-5 up | Make long 3rds (4 blows) | 4-5 down |
| 3rds | 2nds | In the hunt |

✳ And last in this little book two very advanced tricks for you to try:–

## 1-TREBLE BOB on the treble

In 'Kent' and 'Cambridge' and many other minor methods the treble does not PLAIN HUNT, but it TREBLE BOBS, dodging in every place and following a path like this:–

1 2 3 4 5 6

dodge 1-2 up

dodge 3-4 up

dodge 5-6 up

lie

dodge 5-6 down

dodge 3-4 down

dodge 1-2 down

Lead full and dodge 1-2 up

etc

You must first learn to say the places correctly ~ you will never learn to ring it if you get lost counting......

1212 3434 5656 6565 4343 21211......

Stand behind someone else ringing this, say the places and try to see who they are dodging with. When you can see it, then try it!

date you first treble-bobbed

## 2-STEDMAN DOUBLES

Stedman is a 'PRINCIPLE' not a 'METHOD'. All the bells follow the same line, even the treble. Learn this line so well that you can draw it out without hesitation or error.....

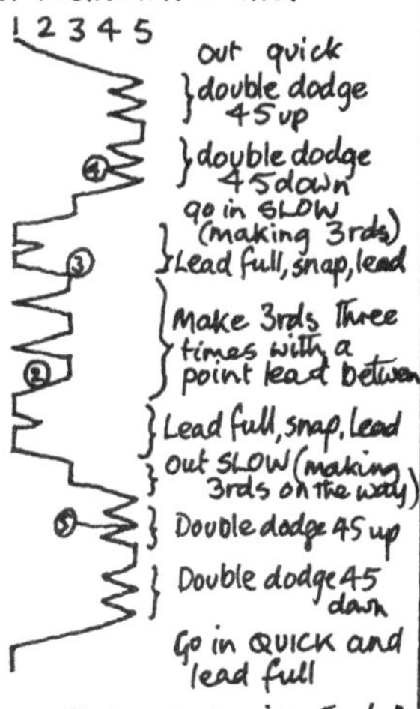


②etc = start point other bells

I suggest that you write out the full course on squared paper. Then you will see which leads are 'wrong' (ie. back + hand). This is an important guide. Watch it then have a go. Listen to those leads!!

date you first rang Stedman.

## •SOME USEFUL BOOKS AND ADDRESSES•

* CENTRAL COUNCIL PUBLICATIONS ~ a wide range of inexpensive booklets + leaflets on all aspects of bells, ringing, towers. See advert. in Ringing World + available from there (address Penmark House, Woodbridge Meadows, Guildford GU1 1BL)

* "Discovering Bells + Bell-Ringing" by John Camp. Published by Shire Publications; excellent cheap book full of information useful for projects/lectures/essays on ringing.

* "Change Ringing" by Wilfred Wilson, published privately from Mrs F. Willgress, 5 Manor Rd, Rushden, Northants, (£14 in 1992) A substantial + readable book which starts where This one does + ends at a very advanced level!

* "The Nine Taylors" by Dorothy L. Sayers. A "who-dunnit" story woven cleverly + knowledgably around bells + ringers + a peal of Kent Treble Bob Major. It won't teach you much about ringing but it is good reading if you like a nice mystery murder!

* "The Ringers Notebook and Diary". Annual diary see advertisement in 'Ringing World' before Christmas. It contains diagrams of many methods, touches, information about Guilds + Associations, record ringing etc. Invaluable!

* "The Ringing World" - weekly magazine published at Penmark House, Woodbridge Meadows, Guildford GU1 1BL Compulsive weekly reading once you are hooked on ringing!

* "A Bellringers Guide to the Church Bells of Britain", by R.H. Dove, available from The Ringing World Office. (£10 in 1992.) Lists in fact all bells in The world hung for change ringing. giving details of weight, note, practice night etc.

* SAYDISC RECORDS, THE BARTON, INGLESTONE COMMON, BADMINTON, GLOS GL9 1BX produce some fine records and cassettes of ringing. Send s.a.e. for details. Instructive listening

* Alan Griffin, Rosebank, Bloxham, Banbury, Oxon OX15 4NA produces various excellent computer programs for BBC micro on tape or disc. Send sae for details. Good teaching tool.

* Mrs S.C. Sotheran, Home Farm, Yearby, Cleveland TS11 8HQ prints your special peals/quarters onto cards. Send a S.a.e for samples. See adverts in Ringing World for prices, etc.

✱ SO HERE WE ARE, on the last page of this little book. No doubt you have done lots of things we have not had space to mention, so here is a checklist to see what you have been up to. Tick those you have done, and try some others....

- [ ] helped spring-clean the ringing chamber
- [ ] rung a quarter-peal
- [ ] been on a ringing outing
- [ ] rung the treble to Little Bob (up to 4th place only)
- [ ] introduced a friend to learn ringing
- [ ] subscribed to The Ringing World (or read someone elses!)
- [ ] learned how to splice a bell rope
- [ ] attended, quite often, the services rung for
- [ ] been a happy and pleasant person in the tower
- [ ] learned to ring a bell up and down
- [ ] acquired a Ringers Diary
- [ ] conducted 120 of any method
- [ ] been present when a stay has been broken
- [ ] seen how a stay is mended
- [ ] been generally on time for practices and Sundays
- [ ] read 'The Nine Taylors' by Dorothy L. Sayers
- [ ] helped check the ropes for wear
- [ ] listened to 'Church Bells on Sunday' Radio 4, 6-45am
- [ ] raised some money for Guild or Tower Bell Repair Fund
- [ ] swept the tower steps (someone has to!)
- [ ] joined your Guild or Association
- [ ] written an article about bells, for church or school mag.
- [ ] put in over 75% attendance at ringing.
- [ ] apologised in advance for absences
- [ ] rung the tenor behind to a doubles method
- [ ] helped put muffles onto the bells
- [ ] rung on half-muffled bells
- [ ] visited a nearby tower for ringing
- [ ] 'stood behind' and followed a new method from the book
- [ ] rung tunes on handbells
- [ ] rung method on handbells
- [ ] been to a Guild or Association Meeting
- [ ] finished everything in this book
- [ ] acquired another book to follow on from this
- [ ] enjoyed yourself most of the time!

## Explanation of the fourth edition

This booklet was written primarily for use by 9-14yr old recruits at Sherbourne, where I have for some years struggled with the problem of putting over the theoretical side of ringing when most elementary books are aimed at adults, and just a mite solid and boring.

The first edition, back in 1982 was just photocopied, onto foolscap paper. By 1985 it was rewritten onto A4 paper with minor additions and amendments making it suitable for young people from 9-90! When Sotherans of Redcar (the friendly bellringers printer) printed the first 2500 we sold out in 3 weeks!

To date 42,500 copies have been sold and the price so far has never been increased.

In 1987 The Follow-on Book was published and in 1988 The Ringers Exercise Book was added to the range of Sherbourne Teaching Aid Books. This is a hobby for me and I aim to make no profit (but do not want to make a loss). So far £12,000 of excess income over expenditure has been handed back to Guild and Association Bell Repair Funds.

Other teaching aids now include a 2-D working model bell, a 'method-maker', a 'listening-aid', leaflets for non-ringers and a Bell Club pack of incentive cards and badges (s.a.e. for prices)

The printer needs to make new plates so I'm taking the opportunity of a new edition with some minor alterations. Thank you to everyone who has been so encouraging.

Pam Copson.

Wellesbourne. 1992